An Omahanui Book

Copyright © 2005 by Tom Downes

First published in Great Britain: May, 2005

Tom Downes asserts his rights
to be identified as the Author of this Work
in accordance with the Copyright, Designs and Patents Act 1988.

British Library Cataloguing in Publication Data

A record for this book is available from the British Library

ISBN 0-9550287-0-1

Typography, and typesetting in Monotype Dante, by Alan Butcher
6 Halepit Road, Gt Bookham, Surrey KT23 4BS

Printed and bound in Great Britain
by Bookmarque Ltd, Croydon, Surrey
Published by
Omahanui Publishing
PO Box 53203
London N3 1JX

RELEASE

YOUR

INNER BEAUTY

TOM DOWNES

OMAHANUI PUBLISHING LONDON

CONTENTS

INTRODUCTION   i

**CHAPTER 1: HOW YOU GRADUALLY
COVERED OVER YOUR INNER BEAUTY**   1

Inner Beauty: Myth or Reality?   2

Inner Beauty – What is it? Who has it?   2

Classical facial features vs. Inner Beauty   4

Dissolving the layers of Mind Cancer   6

Uncover or cover up more Inner Beauty – your choice   7

Inner Beauty & Your Beasts   9

Neutralising life's stresses   10

The Essential education we never received   11

Most of us are barely alive   13

**CHAPTER 2: THE 3-PART PLAN FOR
UNCOVERING YOUR INNER BEAUTY**   16

PART 1: Living in the NOW with PA   19

PART 2: Meditation: the ELIXIRcise of the age!   32

PART 3: Beauty Mind Bathing (BMB)   43

CHAPTER 3:
11 INNER BEAUTY WHOLE-LIFE BONUSES 61

The beauty of increased ENERGY & EFFICIENCY 63

The beauty of increased CONFIDENCE 65

The beauty of increased HEALTH & LONGEVITY 67

The beauty of increased WILLPOWER 69

The beauty of increased PEACE & SERENITY 71

The beauty of increased MEMORY 73

The beauty of increased FRIENDSHIPS & LOVE 75

The beauty of increased WISDOM & INTUITION 77

The beauty of increased CREATIVITY 79

The beauty of increased PROSPERITY 81

The beauty of increased HAPPINESS 83

APPENDIX 85

Notes 98

INTRODUCTION

◆

*'The saying that beauty is but skin deep is but
a skin-deep saying' – John Ruskin*

◆

Your beauty is far more than skin deep, it extends all the way to the heart and mind. This is your truest beauty, your exquisite, shining, child-like beauty that you never lost and still possess. Most of us have just covered it over, but now you can uncover and release it.

I promise to help maximise your facial beauty* by helping release your *Inner Beauty* – your greatest beauty asset. It's a huge promise and not lightly made.

I cannot reshape your eyes, mouth, nose or cheekbones but I can help release your inner radiance to reshape your life. The light in your eye and the way you shone as a child *can* be restored. Your best holiday experiences tell you this is true, when you shed worries and stress to return home completely refreshed, revitalised and looking years younger. That's an *Inner Beauty* effect I'll help you bring back to your everyday life. And that's essential

---

* *This, obviously, excludes facial deformity at birth or through accident or disease for which surgery may better enhance physical beauty.*

because everyday life is far from a holiday. It's just the opposite; with its multiple pressures and emotional stress, it can be a fight that covers increasingly more *Inner Beauty* and prevents it shining through. But now you'll have the tools to counter and dissolve negative influences to maximise your facial beauty.

I'm wary about the use of Botox and facial surgery. What will be their long-term effects? Natural is best. And as you're about to discover, *natural is more beautifying*!

Let's make a pact. You give the *Inner Beauty* practices a fair test for 28 days and I'll not only keep my promise to start you glowing from within, but help release your happiness and whole-life prosperity too.

CHAPTER 1

HOW YOU
GRADUALLY
COVERED OVER
YOUR
INNER BEAUTY

'David is imprisoned in this block of marble;
all I have to do is release him' – Michelangelo

INNER BEAUTY:
MYTH OR REALITY?

You know *Inner Beauty* isn't a myth because you've seen it shining through on to the faces of people who otherwise would not be considered beautiful – but their *Inner Beauty* gloriously beautifies *them*!

You know or will have seen otherwise 'plain' people in their teens, 20s, 30s, 40s, 50s, 60s, 70s and up, who positively glow with *Inner Beauty* and attract like a magnet. That beauty may or may not include personality, charisma and charm but it surpasses all three; for genuine *Inner Beauty* is infused with an unmistakable natural dynamism that's truly wholesome!

INNER BEAUTY: WHAT IS IT?
WHO HAS IT?

Like the oak inside the acorn, every living thing contains within, the whole of its intrinsic Self. In humans, this is our indestructible soul* quality, our highest Self.

Everyone has it and it's the same in everyone, a magnificent attribute that is imperishable. This is our *Inner Beauty*.

---

* *"The Kingdom of God is within you" – Luke 17:21*

It pristinely glows in young children. While growing up, you may have covered it over but it can never be destroyed; it is constant, ageless, and as such can be uncovered and released. You've seen it happen in others to make them shine, and it can happen to you.

True *Inner Beauty* encompasses the essence of every human virtue and positive quality – joy, love, light, peace, serenity, patience, integrity, friendship, kindness, generosity, gratitude, humour, compassion, forgiveness, gentleness, humility, courage, harmony, contentment, willpower and confidence. And it's the sum of all these that lights up your heart and mind, enlivens your whole being and shines through on to your face when you release your *Inner Beauty*.

WANTING BEAUTY IS NATURAL. Nature is full of beauty, nothing is more natural. And it's our *Inner Beauty* that connects with all outer beauty. Why do you love music and art? Because they resonate with your *Inner Beauty*.

Beauty being natural, wanting to reconnect with it is also natural. So we should feel at ease about wanting to maximise our beauty. It's a natural desire unless it turns to vanity; that's an unnatural, self-possessed fixation that repels. True *Inner Beauty* shines and always attracts.

Humility is beautiful, true beauty modest.

*'True beauty must come,
must be grown, from within...'* – Ralph W. Trine

CLASSICAL FACIAL FEATURES VS. INNER BEAUTY

True *Inner Beauty* surpasses classically appealing facial features. That's why we're more attracted to those who glow from within than those with good looks but little else. Of course, if you have both, you're doubly blessed.

Why do you want to be beautiful?

Because it makes you feel confident and good about yourself, and to *attract others*. When true *Inner Beauty* shines through on to the face it appeals instantly to others, attracting the same *Inner Beauty* in each of us. We never tire of witnessing its heart-warming, satisfying zest because it refreshes and energises us. And it does so, even when we just recall it in those of our friends and loved ones who have it.

Is there a paradox, then, about beauty being in the eye of the beholder if personal preferences have us disagreeing about what constitutes beauty, yet we are all drawn to those whose beauty shines from within? The latter seems to be the true and universal *'I'* of the beholder.

UNCOVERING YOUR
INNER BEAUTY
LIFTS YOUR WHOLE LIFE

How much will uncovering and releasing your Inner Beauty affect your outer beauty? Totally! It will maximise your outer beauty as never before. How could it not if your face starts reflecting your magnificent soul qualities. And the less content you are with the facial features Mother Nature gave you, the happier you'll be to have your *Inner Beauty* shine through and make you glow.

Although opposites sometimes attract, by and large, like attracts like. So the amount of *Inner Beauty* you reflect deeply affects your life.

ATTRACTING THE 'RIGHT' PARTNER: If you reflect *Inner Beauty* and its shining qualities then you tend to attract like people and circumstances: friends like you, a partner like you, the 'right' career opportunities that match your qualities, the 'right' whole-life destiny.

And the more 'right' your life goes, the more confident you grow; and the more confident you grow, the more 'right' your life goes. It's the positive upward spiral of success breeding success. Equally, if you exhibit less true inner qualities, then that's what you tend to attract. It works both ways.

5

Is there a downside to a more beautiful you attracting unwanted attention that you might shy away from? Possibly, but the controlled mind and heart that re-establishes *Inner Beauty* also copes more naturally with unwanted attention (see also page 60).

BEWARE THE MIND CANCER THAT COVERS INNER BEAUTY

Most of us suffer from uncontrolled minds and hearts that have the ability to 'eat us up'; inner growths of despairing thoughts and negative emotions we find hard to govern. The psychosomatic power of mind over matter is like a cancer; 'the worry is killing me'* can be literally true. And it can certainly maim your beauty.

YOUR FACE REFLECTS WHAT'S IN YOUR HEART AND MIND. For your *Inner Beauty* to shine through and light up your facial beauty, you need to dissolve the layers of stress, negative emotions and mind rubbish that cover it; layers accumulated over the years. There are proven methods of doing this.

---

* 'At the American Association for the Advancement of Science in Seattle, Prof Arthur Barsky described the "nocebo effect"… the "evil twin" of the placebo. … Dr Barsky, a professor of psychiatry at Harvard Medical School, says that it is no coincidence that people complain about being "scared to death" or "worried sick"…"They're convinced that something is going to go wrong, and it's a self-fulfilling prophecy," he said. … A classic example of the effect was… the Framingham Heart Study: women who believed that they were prone to heart disease were almost four times as likely to die as women with similar risk factors who didn't hold such fatalistic views. In other words, think sick, be sick.' – Roger Highfield, Sunday Telegraph, 22.2.'04.

'Though we travel the world over to find the beautiful, we must carry it with us or we find it not.' – Ralph Waldo Emerson

UNCOVER OR COVER UP MORE INNER BEAUTY; IT'S YOUR CHOICE

There is a law of nature that greatly affects your beauty. This law is *'nothing stays the same'*. It governs every aspect of our lives. We are either getting better or worse, stronger or weaker, at everything we do.

The seasons echo this law: nature bursts alive in spring, peaks in summer, declines through autumn and 'dies' in winter. Plants and animals are 'born', grow to maturity then gradually decline and die. And if, for example, your sight or hearing is impaired or you are prone to anger or self-pity, you will know that it's either getting better or worse.

Because nothing stays the same, your physical beauty – natural ageing aside – either 'increases' or 'decreases' as you go through life. (Or seems to; what actually happens is that your changeless *Inner Beauty* is gradually covered over unless you reverse the trend and uncover it.) The beauty you see in the mirror next year and in five year's time won't be the same as you see today. Joy of joys, it could be *greater*!

For most of us, facial beauty does not increase, it declines, faster or slower depending on our general lifestyle, diet, exercise, sleep and health. But the greatest influence is the state of your mind and emotions* – first and foremost you are what you think and feel.

And although gradual ageing is natural, the release of your unchangeable *Inner Beauty* can dramatically slow the process. That's why some people look 10-20 years younger than they are and why we see shining, blooming beauty in many 50-90 year olds.

While you can exhibit greater facial beauty by releasing more *Inner Beauty*, if you don't do so then your facial beauty must decline because you'll go on covering your *Inner Beauty* deeper and deeper – for nothing stays the same. Clearly, then, how much facial beauty you show is in your control. Your *Inner Beauty* that surpasses facial features is all there deep inside and you can uncover and expose as much as you want.

* *'...people tend to ignore the relationship between mind and body, but there is a connection. Angry, stressed or unstable patients tend to do less well than those who are supported and feel positive'* – Vinod Nargund, leading genital-urinary cancer surgeon, Barts Hospital and The London NHS Trust. *(As reported in the London Evening Standard, 6 October, 2003, by Anastasia Stephens.)*

INNER BEAUTY
& YOUR BEASTS

Negative emotions and negative thinking mask your *Inner Beauty*:

RESENTMENT, ANGER, HATRED, RUDENESS, REVENGE AND VIOLENCE – implant inner hostility, sap energy and build a spiteful, vindictive nature that shows on your face.

JEALOUSY AND ENVY – embitter and dishonour you and your face suffers the consequences.

WORRY AND FEAR - paralyse the mind, blocking ideas for resolving their cause. And your face pays the price.

CRITICISM AND PREJUDICE – create a cynical intolerance that shows on your face.

HYPOCRISY - sullies your integrity and your face can't hide it.

SELF-PITY AND MOODS, GUILT AND REGRETS – debilitate you and lower your dignity. And your face shows it.

GREED, LUST, AND SELFISHNESS – undermine self-respect and alienate friends; your face suffers again.

Each of the above helps create a facial mask that hides your *Inner Beauty*. And every time the negative emotion arises, the mask becomes more firmly fixed. Your health suffers too.

Recently I noticed an otherwise attractive woman wearing just such a mask. She seemed lost in melancholy. But the moment her young daughter came bouncing up, the woman's beauty penetrated the mask and her face momentarily shone. Then when her daughter bounded off again, the mask instantly reappeared and covered her beauty. Like many, she seemed caught in a sorrow that can only worsen unless steps are taken to turn things around. Otherwise habit will tighten the mask and even make it permanent. We've all seen that happen to people.

The way to dissolve negative emotions and thinking is to stop feeding them when they arise; ignore them enough and they won't return. Easily said but so hard to do. Why? Because we have lost control of our hearts and minds, and in so doing, lost control of our beauty.

INNER CITY, INNER BEAUTY: NEUTRALISING LIFE'S STRESSES

'Smile. Tomorrow will be worse.' You need to defuse that wonderful Woody Allen quip by neutralising the stresses of today's demanding world that stifle your *Inner Beauty* and whole quality of life.

Worries and pressures sap energy and health and dull your efficiency which propagates more worries and strains. It's a relentless circular process because there's so much to worry about – finance, partner, family, friends, 'enemies', work, health, sudden crises. Why is it so hard to cope? Because, as noted, we have lost command of our hearts and minds. And if not reversed, the stress *has* to get worse for nothing stays the same.

I vividly recall the time, years ago, when it was suggested to me that most of us are not in control of our minds. I indignantly refuted it. But when I observed my mind at work, I was horrified. I saw that for *most* of the day, *every* day, my mind did its own thing. It controlled me! It was the most shocking realisation of my life. I determined there and then to rectify the situation, and I've never looked back.

ELIMINATING WORRIES. Problems and worries never seem to go away, they just change. Remembering back, you've *always* had problems and worried about them. Yet you always came through – if not totally unscathed. So why not accept this trend. Accept the problems *but eliminate the worry* by regaining heart and mind control. Then you'll start uncovering your *Inner Beauty* to let it shine through on to your face.

THE ESSENTIAL EDUCATION WE NEVER RECEIVED

Because the heart and mind are so powerful, when under control you can achieve virtually anything. But out of control, you can destroy virtually anything.

Scientists say we use only 5-20% of our potential mind power. It's hardly surprising, for you may have had a good education but who taught you how to control your heart and mind? No one. It's the most essential education we *never received* when we were children or through our teens, twenties and upwards.

And over the years we've lost *increasingly more* control because, as we established, if things don't get better they get worse. Were this not so, you could simply 'flick a switch' in the mind and heart and command them to instantly cease all negativity. But you can't, can you?

This habit of heart/mind loss governs our lives. Day in and day out, you don't rule your mind, *your mind rules you!*

This lack of heart/mind control must be the most shocking failing the human race faces. Your whole well being depends on the state of your emotions and thinking: your efficiency, ability to achieve and prosper, be happy and healthy, to learn, create, resolve problems, attract friends and partner, and to interrelate with others; (and globally, our combined ability to prevent hostility and warfare). Fortunately you can reverse this deplorable situation and transform your life by changing your habits. And in so doing, uncover and release your *Inner Beauty*.

◈

'No one would leave a car running in the garage all night, but we let our minds run on... No wonder we often feel tired and dispirited!'
– Eknath Easwaran

MOST OF US ARE
BARELY ALIVE

Try this experiment: while looking at the seconds hand on your watch, reflect that life exists only in each momentary second that passes. All previous seconds are in the past and as such are dead. And the seconds to come are still in the future and equally dead – until they arrive. Life exists only in each present moment *NOW, NOW, NOW* ...*

So?

So if your mind is not present in each moment *NOW*, you are barely alive. Sure, your heart keeps beating but that works automatically.

The shocking thing is, most people's minds for most of the time are not in the present moment *NOW*. They constantly flit to the past and the future, from thought to thought, all day long.

So?

Well, do you tell your mind to flit about, thinking this and that? No, mostly you don't. Observe your mind and see. You don't

---

* It appears that the very opposite is true of the quip 'God invented time to stop everything happening at once.' Einstein said, 'People like us, who believe in physics, know that the distinction between past, present and future is only a stubbornly persistent illusion.'

control it, *your mind controls you! All day long, all night long!*

OK. But does it matter?

Yes! This shocking situation isn't just stifling your beauty, it's stifling your whole life – in two ways:

One, if your mind controls you, how can you overcome stress or change any negative emotions and thinking habits that cover your *Inner Beauty* and affect your happiness and whole-life prosperity?

Two, if you aren't fully 'here' in each present moment, then you aren't fully alive because, as we've seen, life exists only in each NOW. True beauty shines full of life, but how can you shine if not fully alive?

As a young child, you lived fully in each moment NOW all the time. That's why young children shine with such exuberance and life. That's why they're so beautiful, their true *Inner Beauty* isn't covered over.

But at around 4 to 5 years of age, the *uncontrolled* thinking begins, and because nothing stays the same, as we start to grow up, through habit we increasingly lose the ability to be and live in the present all the time.

Don't believe that young children have their innocent beauty merely because their lives aren't yet filled with responsibilities, disappointments and worries. There's more to

14

it than that. Most older children, teenagers and adults worry because through increasing loss of presence of mind they lose control, and then cares control them. Restore this natural, child-like presence of mind, living in each moment fully, and your life changes dramatically for the better. *100% better and more!*

By our present time of life, most of us *think* and *emote* all day long – mostly completely *uncontrolled*. And it's this that covers over your *Inner Beauty* and diminishes your facial beauty.

The 3-Part *Inner Beauty Plan* can turn your life around. Out-sparring the spa and with a decided edge over the scalpel, it is the ultimate interior makeover that releases more *Inner Beauty* to beautify your face the more it's practised.

CHAPTER 2

THE 3-PART PLAN FOR UNCOVERING & RELEASING YOUR INNER BEAUTY

*'Drink deeply from the fountains of beauty
and you cannot help reflecting it.'*
– Eileen Caddy ('Opening Doors Within')

The 3-part *Inner Beauty Plan* uses the mighty potency of your mind and heart; neutralising their *destructive* powers and harnessing their *constructive* ones. Here's why the *Plan* is so effective:

Being the sum of our natural, true soul qualities, our *Inner Beauty* relentlessly presses from within to be released – despite our on-going neglect in covering it over. When we bring these *Inner Beauty* practices into play, they press from the 'outside' to penetrate all the layers of mind and heart rubbish accumulated over the years that we discussed in Chapter One.

It's rather like a road tunnel under construction in the Alps. The tunnelers excavate towards each other from both ends until they eventually meet.

Similarly, as we penetrate the mind/heart coverings, your *Inner Beauty* starts to break through, your face illuminates from within. That's the beauty of the *Plan*, it's a natural process; Mother Nature wants to release its *Inner Beauty* and the 3-part *Plan* dutifully steps in to accelerate the process.

PART 1: Living in the NOW with *PA*   Page 19

PART 2: MEDITATION   Page 32

PART 3: BEAUTY MIND BATHING (BMB) Page 43

CHAPTER 2
THE 3-PART INNER BEAUTY PLAN

PART 1:

LIVING IN THE
NOW
WITH PA

*'Let us not look back in anger or forward in fear,
but around in awareness'* – James Thurber

POSITIVELY VIBRANT!

Imagine how alive and glowing you will be when a new light in the eye replaces the usual everyday dull-eyed persona governed by uncontrolled drifting thoughts and emotions; when you sparkle with the recaptured young child quality of living fully in each moment *NOW*. You'll start to shine and radiate the same *Inner Beauty 'lifeliness'* to maximise your facial beauty.

Welcome aboard, that's where you're headed.

The *PA* practice remedies the lifetime habit of losing control of your powerful mind and heart that we discussed in Chapter One. With control restored, you start accessing your boundless mind / heart potential to invigorate your life on all fronts.

TIMELESS SIMPLICITY. The joy of the *PA* is that it is easy to do, takes not a single extra moment of your time, and you can use it all day long for every activity. It increases you awareness, liveliness and efficiency to such a high degree, it changes everything in your life for the better while increasing your beauty.

Too good to be true? It gets better.

Whenever you notice your mind drifting off into uncontrolled thoughts, use the *PA* to return to the life-filled

present moment *NOW*. With practice, you'll increase yo[ur]
moments of child-like *NOW*ness to enable your *Inner Beauty* to
shine through and enliven your face.

THE *PA* TECHNIQUE: With every activity you
perform, there is a specific point where the 'work' of the activity
takes place. I call this point the *POINT* of *ACTION* (*PA*). Consider
two simple examples: the *PA* when brushing your teeth is the exact
point where the ends of the bristles touch the teeth at every
stroke; when cutting bread, the *PA* is the exact point where the
sharp edge of the knife touches the bread at every stroke.

INCREASED AWARENESS & BEAUTY. When
performing an activity – *any* and *every* activity – if you focus your
mind – i.e. put your attention – on the *PA* of the activity, you
instantly come into the *NOW*. Your mind is compelled to stop
drifting off and instead exerts *NOW*ness.

This life-changing, beautifying *PA* technique is ingenious
because it's so simple. Note that you don't have to actually see the
PA. Indeed, with many activities you cannot; you 'see' it just in the
mind's eye. The above teeth-brushing and bread-cutting examples
are good instances.

**THERE IS NOTHING MYSTICAL ABOUT HOW
THE *PA* WORKS**. You experience increased awareness and
efficiency whenever you do something with concentrated

21

attention. Achievers in sports, business, science and the arts are renowned for this ability. And in emergencies like a fire, this sharp focusing of mind forces itself upon us. So, nothing new here, the *PA* capitalises on a natural phenomenon.

The more you use the *PA*, the more you squeeze out of your life those moments of damaging, uncontrolled negative emotions and thoughts, because your time becomes occupied with non-thinking* *NOW* moments. It's all about habit; changing your habit of uncontrolled mind to controlled mind. That's how you help dissolve the layers of worry and stress covering your *Inner Beauty* to enable it to shine through.

A NEW SUPER-EFFICIENT YOU. All your abilities increase because *NOW*-centred living keeps you focused in a sharpened, one-thing-at-a-time regime. Your new alertness has you better meeting the modern demands of juggling several things 'at once'. You are able to give each need full-focused attention before switching to the next. You gain *extra* energy too because NOW-centredness equals life presence equals energy.

So if you're determined to release your *Inner Beauty*, 'make the vow to stay in the *NOW*'. Use the *PA* all the time until it becomes a habit.

* I am not suggesting leaving the mind blank but filling it with the ever-renewing and refreshing moment-to-moment awareness of your actions and surroundings that you perceive through your reawakened NOWness.

'A child walks with its mother. It sees an oily rainbow on the road,
a leaf, veined and dappled, on the path, a puddle full of clouds,
a smiling dog, a cat that needs to be stroked,
a builder's van all a-rattle, a gentle robin. What did you see?'
– Peter Gray

IDENTIFYING THE **PA**
FOR EACH ACTIVITY

The positions of most *PA*s for most activities are usually fairly obvious. And there is no questioning the subtle yet powerful quality you experience when successfully 'locking into' the *PA* of an activity: your senses sharpen and expand; the periphery of your vision widens, and your hearing heightens as the mind stills.

In short, connected to life, you come alive as your awareness expands.

LINKING ALL ACTIVITIES INTO
ONE CONTINUOUS **NOW**

If every time you return to the *NOW* you reconnect with life and *Inner Beauty*, imagine the beautifying power of *continuous*, childlike *NOW*ness, The following *PA*s for everyday activities help you achieve it.

It may seem strange applying the *PA* to mundane activities like washing up, talking, ironing, brushing teeth, and walking. But it's your ordinary daily, repetitive occurrences requiring the least attention that build your deeply ingrained habit of mind/heart drift. And because, as we saw in Chapter One, nothing stays the same, if you don't remedy the situation, it *has* to get worse.

THE BEAUTY OF ATTENTIVE
SPEAKING & LISTENING

Most of us can be poor listeners, listening without hearing as heart and mind wander off unchecked to their other priorities, weakening the *NOW*ness habit. But using the *PA* compels you into the *NOW*.

When conversing, without losing normal eye contact, focus on hearing the actual *sound* of the speaker's voice – including your own – rather than the actual words. This point of sound is the *PA* for talking and listening. Keep returning your attention to it when you notice your mind drifting away.

When you talk, focusing on the sound of your own voice sharpens its clarity and your articulation, and increases the attention of your listeners. Try it, prove it for yourself.

When you listen, the *PA* sharpens word distinction and your understanding of the speaker's *thoughts behind the words*, for the voice can communicate more than the words. And sometimes it even contradicts them, i.e. you realise the speaker doesn't mean what (s)he says. The truth behind statements like, 'Oh that's wonderful,' or 'I don't mind at all,' can be *"Oh thanks a lot! H**l, that's all I need!"*

Your sharper listening affects the speaker too; if (s)he's talking distractedly with limited interest, it helps 'wake her/him up', invariably taking the wind out of her/his tales.

Of course, whenever conversing, it's uncaring not to give your full attention. You can usually kindly excuse yourself if you've had enough.

Here's a good tip for calming a heated conversation or adding warmth to it. Simply bring to mind feelings of genuine love for the person in front of you. Invariably you'll see her/his face instantly soften. What happens is that your love thought transmits from your heart to your eyes and (s)he picks it up and instantly reflects it. Try it.

Naturally, using the PA when listening to your favourite music sharpens the experience and increases your enjoyment. Again, simply focus fully on the sound.

A BEAUTIFUL VOICE REFLECTS *INNER BEAUTY*. And because the reverse is true, you can help uncover your *Inner Beauty* by developing the beauty of your voice. Introduce into it genuine feelings of friendliness, kindness, enthusiasm, love, joy and confidence. Record and listen to your voice on a cassette player. Do you like what you hear? If not, work on it. Practice makes perfect.

As with positive thinking, *speaking* positively, joyfully and enthusiastically helps release positivity, joy and enthusiasm. Again, it's your everyday habits that make you what you are.

THE BEAUTY
OF ATTENTIVE EATING

The *PA* when eating and drinking is in your mouth where you taste and chew your food. Focus your mind there to return to the *NOW*. And, of course, to enjoy the fullest taste of your food and to appreciate what your body needs.

Is this important in the grand scale of life? Very, for two reasons.

First, the 70,000 or so meals you pile on to your lifetime plate are grand opportunities to increase or decrease your mind control habit.

Second, you eat and drink to stay alive so it makes sense to do it wisely. Yet most of us eat with little attention. We eat while reading, watching TV, listening to the radio, talking to people, driving the car, walking, or combining two or more of these at once. (No wonder we are surprised sometimes to see an empty plate when we can't recall finishing a snack – *Hey, where did that go?*)

'We are what we eat' is probably second only to 'we are what we think and feel' in life-enhancing priorities. Our eating habits are vital to good health, fitness and longevity. Most agree that a healthy, well-balanced diet promotes beauty. And a prerequisite to sound eating is eating with attention.

Would just eating while doing nothing else be too boring? Is being fit and healthy boring? Or gaining greater control of your heart and mind and glowing with *Inner Beauty* boring? Attentive eating pays off a hundred-fold.

THE BEAUTY OF
ATTENTIVE WALKING

We walk so much in our lives, it's another excellent opportunity to weaken or strengthen our *NOW*ness habit that affects our 'lifeliness' and facial beauty.

The *PA* when walking is where the soles of the shoes touch the ground, and that's where you focus your mind to come into the *NOW*.

When you first try this, don't be surprised (or be put off) if initially your mind 'gets in the way' and your walking feels a little clumsy. You'll soon get the hang of it and appreciate its rich rewards.

It expands awareness, extending your field of vision to encompass more of the left, the centre and the right; your hearing sharpens; your sense of smell heightens; you become more awake, more in touch; brought into the *NOW*, you liven up!

This increased alertness is contrary to what you'll observe

in most people sauntering along. Look and see: a kind of 'sleepwalking' rules the paves where heads full of distracted thinking, zombie forth; people with vacant looks and distorted faces mostly from uncontrolled anxieties and worries.

BEAUTY WALKING: Your new *NOW*ness leaves that behind; you move light-heartedly down the street with the sparkle of a young child appreciating everything all around you, as depicted by Peter Gray on page 23. It's a completely different world in which you turn mundane walking into *Beauty Mind Bathing* (page 43).

You refresh your mind in observing and interconnecting with the world around you – nature, mankind, city-scapes – enjoying rather than tolerating the variety and hustle-bustle of a colourful, constantly-changing show. This wide-awake, *NOW*-centredness ensures that you take in rather than dissipate energy. And that is so beautifying.

MISCELLANEOUS *PA*s

When seeking the *PA* for any activity, look for the precise point where the action of the activity takes place.

Reading: the point on the paper where the eyes meet the printed word.

Writing/drawing/painting: the points where the pen/pencil/brush touch the paper/canvas.

In the kitchen: when peeling, stirring, chopping, washing/drying up, etc., the points where the blade of the peeler removes the peel, the stirring spoon touches the food, the dishcloth and tea towel wipe and dry the plate, etc.

In the garden: when digging, pruning, mowing the lawn, etc., the points where the spade touches and digs down into the earth, the pruner blades cut the plant, the mower blades cut the grass, etc.

In the workshop: when hammering, sawing, chiselling, etc., the points where the hammer hits the nail head, the jagged blade edge saws the wood, the chisel edge cuts into the wood, etc.

In the office: when using the computer, the *PA* will depend on whether you're a touch typist who looks continually at the screen or if you are a two-fingered tyco who looks mostly at the keyboard. If the former, the *PA* is on the screen where each new letter appears. If the latter, the *PA* moves from the points where the fingers touch the keys, to the screen when your eyes lift to check (hope?) you've typed it right.

FOR YOUR BEAUTY'S SAKE, *PA* RULES! OK?

Be patient and persevering with your *PA* practice. After all, it's a long time since you last delighted in the joy and freedom of living continuously in the *NOW*; you were just a young child. And don't snub an activity as too ordinary and unworthy of applying the *PA* to. The less demanding the activity, the easier it is to rest your mind on the *PA*. Then not only does the mundane become less boring, the mind becomes still. And this still quality maintains the effortless constancy of each *NOW* moment.

Yes, you may find that initially the *PA* practice can seem artificial and simplistic. But by instantly bringing you into the *NOW* and increasingly doing so as it becomes a habit, it isn't just beautifying, it is totally life enriching in everything you do.

WHEN THE *PA* TECHNIQUE DISCARDS ITSELF:

When your *NOW* moments become an everyday habit and link together into a continuous chain of through-the-day *NOW*ness, then, paradoxically, the *PA* technique automatically discards itself. You become less and less aware of using it.

This is because when *you are already in the NOW*, your senses are fully outward and connected to life. So the *PA* technique, as such, dissolves and disappears.

Like water wings for learning to swim, and support wheels for learning to bicycle, once the skill has been acquired and fully adopted into 'your system', the supportive technique becomes superfluous and sheds itself like a caterpillar's pupa. The *PA* no longer applies just as it doesn't (and never did) for young bright-eyed children who are naturally in the *NOW* all the time. You return to your natural state of childlike *NOW*ness. That's why it is so beautifying.

And that's a different world altogether to your present one. It's a wonderful, wonder-filled world in which you naturally shine with *Inner Beauty* that illuminates your face; a world in which you see more and more beauty in *everything* around you; a world in which you have more and more fun with *everything* you do.

PART 2:

MEDITATION

'Go placidly amid the noise & haste, & remember
what peace there may be in silence…' – from the Desiderata

THE **ELIXIR**CISE OF THE AGE!

Don't take my word for it, and put aside any preconceived ideas or prejudices you may have. Let the astonishing body of research and the media comments in the appendix do the talking; meditation is the proven 'super elixir' exercise of the age. That's why millions testify to it.

If you are not already meditating, you are depriving yourself of probably the most important health and all-round well-being practice known to mankind. And its potency definitely helps release your *Inner Beauty* to maximise your facial beauty.

Meditation is indispensable to our cause because it helps dissolve the layers of negative emotions and mind rubbish covering your *Inner Beauty* that we discussed in Chapter One.

How does meditation achieve this? Through its enormous and irrefutable (see the research) re-energising, conscious-ness/awareness-lifting, stress-neutralising, joy-releasing power, brought about by stilling and bringing peace to the mind. Just as deep down beneath the choppy surface waves of the ocean, the water is still and calm, the mind too deep down is still. And meditation calms the mind's habitual agitated surface, allowing its deepest powers to be accessed.

IF YOU COULD BOTTLE MEDITATION
IT WOULD BE WORTH A FORTUNE.

A twice-daily dosage invigorates your whole system, physically, mentally and spiritually. It's the proven, genuine pick-me-up cum preventative cure-all. So what are you waiting for? When you start meditating you start releasing your *Inner Beauty* to maximise your outer beauty as well as improving every other aspect of your life.

WHAT MEDITATION
IS NOT

People from all walks of life meditate. It was/is practised by many of history's and today's greatest minds.

It is not a cult or religion and neither does it in any way impair, abuse or impede any religious beliefs.

It is not mysterious, mystical or austere. You don't go into a trance; *you* are in control. It doesn't require special beliefs or postures; you don't have to sit uncomfortably, be a vegetarian or go on a special diet.

Millions, globally, practise it because it works. Meditation is for everyone.

PRACTISING MEDITATION:
GENERAL DIRECTIONS

If you are not already meditating I recommend that you

contact a local meditation centre* or practitioner. Source the Internet (particularly), your local library, newspapers or phone directories.

Otherwise start today with one of the two traditional meditations outlined on page 38 – Mantra and Breathing.

First though, four important points:

1. MEDITATION FREQUENCY

Ideally meditate twice a day - morning and evening – *every* day. Make it part of your daily routine and it will transform your life.

The morning meditation prepares your mind for the day's challenges. You probably eat breakfast yet it's even more important to nourish your mind than your body. And it helps release your *Inner Beauty*.

The evening meditation helps neutralise the day's frustrations and stresses, draws in fresh energy and instils peace. Spending a few minutes afterwards reflecting on the day is useful too; sometimes fruitful new perspectives on events are revealed.

The best times to meditate are around sunrise and sunset, nature's periods of natural stillness that we can harmonise with. If you can't manage these, choose times to suit your daily routine;

---

* *You benefit in at least two ways by belonging to an organisation: you are more inclined to keep up your daily practice, and the depth and quality of meditation increases with the greater numbers participating, thus accelerating your meditation development.*

but try to keep to the same times every day because it creates an orderly, rhythmic pattern that the mind enjoys. (Though, of course, it happily adjusts to sensible flexibility.) It is beneficial meditating just before going to bed as well, if only for a few minutes; there's nothing like putting your mind and heart to rest before your body. Try it, you'll sleep better and wake more refreshed.

2. LENGTH OF MEDITATION

I recommend that you meditate for 20 - 30 minutes per session. If you initially find this too long, meditate for just 10 minutes for the first week or so. I suggest you *don't* meditate for longer than 30 minutes per session unless guided by a meditation practitioner. (Though I'm aware of no ill effects from meditating for longer periods.)

3. WHERE TO MEDITATE

Ideally, always meditate in the same place and if possible dedicate that place solely to meditation because over a period of time you build up subtle vibrations there that contribute to more efficient on-going meditation. Your chosen place should be as quiet and peaceful as possible and be clean, tidy and uncluttered. All that said, meditating *any*where is better than not meditating at all. Open a window and keep the room well aired.

If you meditate on a chair, ideally choose a straight-back

dining type, armless or armed, as you prefer. If you opt for a lotus position or another sitting/kneeling position, that's fine provided you can comfortably maintain it for the meditation duration.

4. OVERCOMING DISTRACTIONS

Meditation exposes multiple distractions that merely confirm our need for mind and heart control.

i)The Mind Runs Amock: Typically, you are bombarded with multiple thoughts. So many that you may feel that meditation makes heart and mind control worse, not better. This is not so. Because the mind is more sharply focused, meditation simply highlights distractions. Allow the thoughts to come and go. If you try too hard to *not* think about them, you energise and prolong their stay.

Keep returning the mind to the point of focus – see 'method' on page 40. Don't give in, don't get up. persevere and exert your willpower. Hey, who's in charge here, you or your mind? Meditation merely highlights the mind's uncontrolled habbit of wandering; be grateful for this reminder and be motivated to reverse the trend. If you don't, it will get worse because, as seen, nothing stays the same.

Know that with practice it is possible to reach undistracted single-pointedness, and that can turn you into a powerhouse.

ii) Extraneous Sounds: Sounds from every quarter will seek your attention. As with the thoughts, don't try too hard not to listen. 'Watch' them neutrally, passively, patiently, and keep returning your mind to the point of focus – see 'method' – p.40.

iii) Bodily Discomforts: Parts of the body may itch and demand to be scratched. Hard though it be, try to resist. Once you start it's hard to stop, but resist with willpower and the itches decline. Keep returning your mind to the point of focus – see 'method' on page 40.

iv) Drowsiness: You may feel drowsy and even doze off. Don't worry, it happens to us all. Keeping the room aerated and not too warm helps prevent this.

CHOOSE EITHER THE **MANTRA** OR **BREATHING** MEDITATION

The two Meditations I recommend are the Mantra Meditation and Breathing Meditation. I offer these because they are universally practised with great success by millions around the world and can be used anywhere besides the usual home environment.

OPTION 1: **MANTRA** MEDITATION

In mantra meditation, a sound or combination of sounds is silently repeated. In some meditation centres, individuals are given a specific, personal (though not usually unique) mantra.

The word mantra is variously described in the original Sanskrit language as 'a sacred text, incantation, prayer, song of praise/magical formula to acquire superhuman powers.'

Perhaps the most famous and most powerful mantra is Om (Aum). This is said to be the primal sound of the universe, that which brought it into being and upholds it.

You may beneficially choose for a mantra, a word (or words) that is/are sacred or devotional to you personally. It/they might be chosen from one of the religions.

For example 'Jesus', 'Lord', 'Mary', 'Krishna', 'Heavenly Father' or 'Divine Mother'; or simply be an uplifting word that fills you with positivity. For example 'love', 'joy', 'peace' or 'beauty'.

As you might expect, the more sacred and devotional mantras are felt to be more powerful than the latter.

The power of Mantra Meditation lies in the actual word or phrase chosen, its repetitious vibration and the depth of concentration brought to bear on it.

Mantra meditation: PREPARATION & METHOD

1. Remove shoes and sit forward and upright so as not to lean on back of chair, (if using chair). Keep spine vertically straight but not stiff, with shoulders back and stomach in; feet flat on floor – not crossed – with legs vertical; hands in lap or on thighs; look straight ahead. Relax but keep alert.

2. Close your eyes.

3. Silently repeat your mantra for 10-30 minutes.

4. Keep your mind focused throughout at the point between your eyebrows – the 'third eye'.*

5. Allow the body to become as still as possible.

6. When thoughts or outside sounds enter the mind, gently let them go, and keep returning to the mantra.

OPTION 2:
BREATHING MEDITATION

In Breathing Meditation you concentrate not on a sound but on your incoming and outgoing breath.

Preparation & Method:

1. Remove shoes and sit forward and upright so as not to lean on back of chair, (if using chair). Keep spine vertically straight

---

* This is the point, by polarity, to the medulla oblongata at the base of the brain where the skull joins the back of the neck and where consciousness enters the body. (And also where consciousness leaves the body; hence the upturned eyes at death.)

but not stiff, with shoulders back and stomach in; feet flat on floor – not crossed – with legs vertical; hands in lap or on thighs; look straight ahead. Relax but keep alert.

2. Close your eyes.

3. Keep your mind focused on the rise and fall of your breath.

4. Allow your body to become as still as possible.

5. When thoughts or outside sounds enter the mind, gently let them go, and keep returning your attention to your breathing.

COUNTERING THE 4 FAVOURITE EXCUSES FOR NOT MEDITATING

1. 'I Haven't got time.'

Meditation gives you back far more time than it takes by increasing your awareness and efficiency, neutralising your stress, and raising your energy. Your peace, happiness, good health and general wellbeing are greatly enhanced too. You haven't got time not to meditate!

2. 'I can't sit still for long.'

If you are that restless then your mind and heart definitely need the benefits of meditation. And the longer you leave it, the worse you'll become because of the law of 'nothing stays the same'.

3. 'When I meditate my mind runs amok.'

Keep returning the mind to the point of focus – see page 37.

4. 'Meditation is boring.'

Yes, sitting still doing nothing can seem boring initially. But how boring is being unable to access your *Inner Beauty* to maximise your facial beauty, and realising your whole-life happiness and prosperity? Persevere and you will find meditation relaxing, beautifying and totally fulfilling.

MEDITATION & PRAYER

No discussion on *Inner Beauty* can exclude the power of prayer because prayer has been proven effective – even to people who consider themselves non-religious – to billions over the ages. Some say that prayer is talking to God and meditation listening to Him. Be that as it may, if you believe in prayer do use it. If you don't, then enjoy the benefits of meditation because as Maureen Cleave says in the index on page 89, 'You don't have to believe in it... if you do it, it will work.'

PART 3:

BEAUTY
MIND BATHING

> *'Man's mind, once stretched to a new idea,
> never regains its original dimensions.'*
> – Oliver Wendell Holmes

Just as a deep soak in a hot bath helps dissolve the day's layers of frustrations and stress, **Beauty Mind Bathing** (**BMB**) helps dissolve the de-beautifying layers of accumulated mind and heart rubbish we identified.

As you will recognise, you already **Beauty Mind Bathe** in many ways. I merely extend these to build up your beauty bank with natural, confidence-inducing exercises. Practised regularly, they dissipate beauty-lack thoughts, helping you see for yourself that you truly do possess a fount of glowing *Inner Beauty* that can be uncovered and released to shine through every pore.

7 BMB PRACTICES

There are seven BMB practices/situations:

1. Creative Visualisations & Affirmations;

2. Beauty Reading, Viewing, and Listening; and
   the Beauty & Happiness Scrapbooks;

3. Beauty Visiting;

4. Beautiful Environment and Good Company;

5. Personal Activities;

6. Beauty Introspection;

7. Setting & Achieving Goals.

BMB PRACTICE 1
CREATIVE VISUALISATIONS & AFFIRMATIONS

Creative visualisation is the self-motivating aid that works by harnessing your mind power to *think* yourself *already* succeeding and achieving objective(s) *before* you start the action.

Everything that's made and created happens in mind first; what your mind can visualise, you can activate to bring into being. Creative visualisation is used in healing, sports, business, and wherever people strive to attain goals. Millions around the world have proven it works. Small wonder, then, that Shakti Gawain's book *Creative Visualization* has sold over two million copies. And Dina Glouberman's book, *Life Choices, Life Changes* adds a further dimension to Shakti's. I recommend both.

AFFIRMATIONS are the repetitive use of positive words or phrases – spoken aloud or silently within – to strongly affirm your objective(s). They work powerfully in conjunction with visualisations or by themselves. Repeated affirmations enter first the subconscious mind, and as they go deeper, the super-conscious* mind where their influencing effect take full reign.

* i) 'Professor Jules-Bois of the Sorbonne said in 1928 that French psychologists have investigated and accorded recognition to the superconsciousness. He said, 'The existence of a superconscious mind has long been recognized philosophically, being in reality the Over-Soul spoken of by Emerson; but only recently has it been recognised scientifically." ii) In "The Over-Soul," Emerson wrote: "A man is the façade

NEGATIVE AFFIRMATIONS: Many people use negative affirmations without realising it or appreciating how much they undermine self-confidence. If you carry around thoughts like *'People think... I'm fat ...I'm thin ...I'm shy ...I'm short ...I'm (too) tall ...I'm ugly ...I'm 'dumb' ...I'm strange ...I'm useless,* then people's minds will pick up on it and they will think just that. Equally if you think 'I'm bound to make a mess of this,' or *'(s)he'll think I'm a fool,'* its repetitious force can help make it happen! You need to overpower negative affirmations with positive ones.

BMB **VISUALISATIONS & AFFIRMATIONS** use specific images of beauty, happiness and other life-enhancing qualities that are personally appealing and meaningful.

They are also particularly helpful for those trying times like the need to dissolve unpleasant memories, divorce, loss of a loved one or a job, and moving house. (See appendix pages 92-95.)

What we each consider beautiful and makes us happy will be personal but might include: the specific beauties of spring, summer, autumn and winter; beautiful gardens and scenery;

of a temple wherein all wisdom and all good abide." iii) "Our conscious and subconscious being is crowned by a superconsciousness," Rabbi Israel H. Levinthal pointed out in a lecture in New York. "Many years ago the English psychologist, F. W. H. Myers, suggested that 'hidden in the deep of our being is a rubbish heap as well as a treasure house.'...the new psychology of the superconscious focuses its attention upon the treasure house – the region that alone can explain the great, unselfish, heroic deeds of men." iv) 'Superconscious perceptions of truth are permanently real and changeless.' – Paramahansa Yogananda. [All of i) – iv) above are from 'Autobiography of a Yogi' by Paramahansa Yogananda.]

'beautiful' people from the past and present, in character and achievements; beautiful pets and wildlife, arts and crafts, architecture and inventions, cars, yachts, planes, fashion. Anything goes, it's beauty through your eyes.

Choosing one subject at a time, close your eyes and bathe in its beauty by visualising it deeply and fully. Note, as appropriate, its form and features, elegance, grace, strength, agility, speed, dexterity, brilliance and subtleties of colour and texture. If relevant, imagine its sounds, smells and tastes too, for the more senses you bring into play, the more powerfully visualisation works. Being subjects that you love and make you happy, just bringing them to mind will light you up.

Make a habit of spending a few minutes on visualisations and affirmations daily, and you'll start to sense a new inner positivity that releases increasingly more *Inner Beauty*. It's an excellent 'filler' exercise when commuting, queuing or waiting for the kettle to boil. An extension to the practice is visualising yourself in a mood-lifting scenario like the examples given in the appendix on pages 90 and 91 – *Walking Through a Garden Paradise, and a Pacific Island Shangri-la.*

BEAUTY READING, VIEWING & LISTENING, & BEAUTY/HAPPINESS SCRAPBOOKS

Beauty Mind Bathing offers a thousand *Inner Beauty*-releasing opportunities with reading, viewing and listening.

UPLIFTING READING MATTER

There's a wealth of inspiring pictorial images to suit everyone's interests in books and magazines filled with beautiful, fascinating and humorous pictures: exquisite scenery, buildings, the customs of different countries, gardening, architecture, arts, crafts, hobbies, animals, sea life, fashion, interior and exterior design, sports; every subject imaginable.

Then there are all the uplifting non-pictorial fiction and non-fiction books including poetry, self-help, biography, travel and humour. Humour is an especially beautifying misery-buster. Libraries and bookshop are mines of inspiration. **Beauty Mind Bathe** regularly with an inspiring or exhilarating good read.

Although also uplifting, newspapers can bring dispiriting news too. While it's healthy to be aware of the world's troubles don't be caught in the gloom. If we can help others we should. If we can't, it doesn't help to add to universal despondency.

We owe it to ourselves, family, friends, neighbours and the world at large, to stay in as good a cheer as possible.

HAPPINESS/BEAUTY SCRAPBOOKS

Collect pictures of the beautiful things that inspire you, and paste them up in scrapbooks. Include jokes, anecdotes, positive proverbs and sayings, poetry – whatever uplifts you.

Look at them often, particularly when you're down; they can quickly pick you up and get you back on a positive track. I can't say it enough: **it's what you do every day that makes you what you are!**

The more you return to your true inner nature of happiness, the more happiness – and *Inner Beauty* – you release. Remember, happiness is always a process of returning 'home'. That's why you like it.

PHOTO ALBUMS

These can be uplifting and lots of fun. But don't fall into the trap of sentimental reminiscing. Pondering on '*if only*' what-might-have-been can lead to self-pity that covers up more *Inner Beauty* and opposes your living-in-the-*now PA* development.

Nostalgia is only healthy when it positively lifts the heart and mind like recalling past successes to buck you up, or uncritically reflecting on past 'mistakes' to prevent them recurring.

WATCHING TV

There's a gamut of TV programmes. Be selective. What does a programme contribute to your mind and heart? Is it uplifting or depressing, mind-challenging or dulling? Is it releasing or covering your *Inner Beauty*?

At what point does reasonable, restorative TV escapism from a tiring day become time-wasting lethargy?

It matters because we spend nearly 4 hours a day, on average, watching TV – almost a quarter of your non-sleeping life! Even a little of that spent daily on these *Inner Beauty* practices will increase your facial beauty. Again, it's about your *every*day habits working for or against you.

VIDEOS, DVDs, CINEMA & THEATRE

The same standards apply as for TV. There are truly entertaining and uplifting films and plays to **Beauty Mind Bathe** in. Discrimination is the key to uncovering rather than covering more of your *Inner Beauty*.

LISTENING TO MUSIC & RADIO PROGRAMMES

Whether live or recorded, listening to music has to be one of our most fruitful and enjoyable **Beauty Mind Bathing** experiences. If you ever feel down, listen to music that lifts you back to your true inner joy. 'Talking book' tapes and radio programmes can also be uplifting.

BEAUTY VISITING

You **Beauty Mind Bathe** every time you experience mind refreshment at art galleries, museums, public gardens and parks, the seaside, countryside, riverside and any place that provides enriching beauty. What could be more natural?

Going away on holiday is an excellent **BMB** practice. You usually return relaxed, refreshed, re-energised, healthier and happier. Of course, the new beauty friends and family see in your face is released *Inner Beauty*. Your features haven't changed, (except you may have a tan). What happens is that when accumulated worries and tiredness dissolve, your natural *Inner Beauty* shines through. This 'glowing holiday' effect is the *3-Part Inner Beauty Plan*'s aim for *every*day living.

Make the most of your breaks to revitalise yourself – from the *inside out*!

BEAUTIFUL ENVIRONMENT & GOOD COMPANY

Your environments and the people you live, work and 'play' with affect your well being and hence your beauty. After all, they constitute *most of your life*! So live in the best dwelling and neighbourhood you can afford, and choose good company.

I recommend the practice of de-junking your home of 'stuff' you no longer use. It helps de-clutter the mind. *Simple is freeing, simple is best.*

If we associate with people of weak morals we weaken ourselves. So choose the good company of honest, upright, positive and happy people because they reflect your *Inner Beauty* qualities and help you release them.

Steer clear of habitual doubters and pessimists who can unsettle and infest you with their downbeat thoughts and opinions. Their depressing views are debilitating and contagious.

BMB PRACTICE 5

PERSONAL ACTIVITIES

If you love a sport, hobby or special interest, (providing it's not offensive or damaging to others), pursue it with zest. Bathe in the beautiful way it lights up your mind and invigorates your life. For what is in your heart will give you joy and satisfaction that help uncover your *Inner Beauty*; the joy without meets the joy within.

THE BEAUTY
OF INTROSPECTION

1. TREATMENT OF YOURSELF & OTHERS:

Introspection, the self-analysis of your lifestyle, is an important aspect of **Beauty Mind Bathing**. You hinder the release and cover more of your *Inner Beauty* if you engage in *outer non-beauty*, i.e. thinking and doing things that oppose your true inner qualities.

How do you treat others and yourself with regards fairness, honesty, your help and time, forgiveness, love, kindness, patience and gratitude?

Are you considerate or demanding, friendly or hostile, loyal or disloyal, courageous or cowardly, hardworking or lazy, generous or mean, kind or cruel, creative or destructive, encouraging or critical, reasonable or stubborn, discreet or indiscreet, decisive or procrastinating?

Effective, healthy introspection is *positive* self-analysis, not negative self-criticism. So make constructive changes where you feel you should but be patient with yourself.

2. DISSOLVING NEGATIVE EMOTIONS:

I touched on this in Chapter One. The poison of negative emotions smothers *Inner Beauty* and can seriously damage your health. Neutralise them with this 8-step formula:

i) Say to yourself, *'Stop it NOW! This* .... (name the negative emotion) *is further covering my Inner Beauty.'*

ii) Look in the mirror to see how ugly the negative emotion is. Smile, (force yourself to, if need be). Note the beautifying smile compared to the ugly emotion.

iii) Count your blessings.

iv) Visualise yourself in a positive, happy frame of mind, *not* reacting jealously / other negative (as applicable).

v) Repeat the affirmation: *'I am putting* .... (name the negative emotion) *out of my life forever, and replacing it with my true inner happiness.'*

vi) Read your goals, (page 56). Visualise yourself achieving them. This diminishes the negative emotion.

vii) Read your Beauty / Happiness Scrapbooks, (page 49).

viii) Practise the *PA* to eliminate the uncontrolled thoughts and emotions.

RESENTMENT, ANGER, HATRED and VIOLENCE:

These begin to dissipate when you catch their starting point – often the ego defending an idea about itself: *'How dare you!'* Remind yourself that the emotion will dissolve eventually – they always do – so make it *now*!

Suppressing emotion isn't the answer or, like a volcano,

you will eventually erupt. Don't allow the emotion to arise by regaining mind and heart control with the *3-Part Inner Beauty Plan*. Practise the 8 steps, above.

GRUDGES AND REVENGE: What you sow you reap. Best to forgive and forget and reap your *Inner Beauty*. Practise the 8 steps, above.

JEALOUSY: Over-possessiveness is unreasonable. You can't own anyone. It's unnaturally constricting and sure to end in turmoil. Practise the 8 steps, above.

ENVY: However much you have (or don't have), there's always someone with more (and with less). Turn envy on its head by admiring the envied one for what they have. Practise the 8 steps, above.

WORRY AND FEAR: These are the mind and heart out of control. Practise the 8 steps, above, and don't avoid but face your challenges squarely, taking every necessary action you can.

CRITICISM AND PREJUDICE: These dissolve when you accept people for what they are, seek the best in them, and forgive them their 'faults'. Practise the 8 steps, above.

HYPOCRISY: The more we realise our magnificent soul qualities – page 3 – the less we'll want to say one thing and do another. Practising the *3-Part Inner Beauty* exercises uncovers these qualities.

SELF-PITY AND MOODS: Feeling sorry for yourself is a corrosive, living-in-the-past emotion that you hate yourself for afterwards. Moodiness is a self-absorbed trait that's often inflicted on others which is unacceptably selfish. Practise the 8 steps on page 54.

GUILT AND REGRETS: For anything you've done – perhaps even long ago – that you're ashamed of, make amends if possible. Forgive yourself and let it go now. The event was 'bad', not you. Having regrets is living in the past and burns precious energy. Move on. Practise the 8 steps on page 54.

GREED, LUST AND SELFISHNESS: These self-centred cravings can never be appeased; only mining your inner happiness brings true, on-going satisfaction. Rein in your desires. Practise the 8 steps on page 54.

BMB PRACTICE 5

THE BEAUTY OF SETTING & ACHIEVING GOALS

There's nothing like the success of achieving goals and realising more of your full potential to make you really shine. It's a thing of beauty in its own right.

Ask yourself what you want with your personal, family and career life in, say, one, three, six and twelve year's time? Write down your goals in a precise single statement:

'In .... year's time I shall: ....

....

....

....

....

(complete for 1, 3, 6 & 12* years for each of career, personal, family & other appropriate areas of your life.)

Write down the steps you will take and any sacrifices, if necessary, you'll make to meet your goals. Then work your plan. Bring the plan to mind several times a day to implant it firmly in your subconscious and superconscious mind where it will create ideas to aid their progress. Your goals will help uplift you when life gets frustrating and difficult.

How *high* should you set your goals? There are two schools of thought on this: one, keep them realistically attainable; two, reach for the stars! It depends on personal temperament so the choice is yours.

Check your progress frequently. If changing circumstances suggest adjustments to your goals, be flexible and adjust. If you

---

* *In his book 'Autobiography of a Yogi', Paramahansa Yogananda wrote: 'The ancient rishis discovered that man's earthly and heavenly environment, in a series of twelve-year cycles, push him forward on his natural path.' And the author's basic research of asking people he meets tends to confirm that major life-changing occurrences happen to most of us within a year or two either side of our twelfth, twenty-fourth, thirty-sixth, forty-eighth, sixtieth, etc. birthdays.*

don't fully meet some goals, analyse why and make necessary changes. Have no regrets; move on positively.

Setting goals and starting on a course of action attracts favourable circumstances like a magnet. W H Murray wrote: *'The moment one definitely commits oneself, then Providence moves too. All sorts of things occur to help one that would never otherwise have occurred.'* A goals-centred life is more exciting and exhilarating too. Somerset Maugham said, *'It's a funny thing about life; if you refuse to accept anything but the best, you very often get it.'*

'We are what we think. All that we are arises with our thoughts.'
– The Buddha

THE 3-PART INNER BEAUTY EXERCISES
AFTERWORD

1. BEAUTY & PERSEVERANCE

For your outer beauty's sake, don't neglect your *Inner Beauty* practices. Doing even one of the three helps release *Inner Beauty*. Of course, what you put in you get back; greater input gives a greater return.

If you start with enthusiasm and fall by the wayside that's OK. Don't persecute, persevere, the benefits are worth their wait in gold.

28 DAYS TRIAL: Do try all three practices faithfully for 28 days. See how they make you look and feel. After that, if tempted to give them a miss, take these two 'shake-me-up, wake-me-up' tests:

MIRROR TEST: Look in the mirror and ask yourself how important it is to **look your most beautiful** right now, and for the rest of your life. *Nothing* will maximise your facial beauty more than releasing your *Inner Beauty*. Keep on with the *Plan* and you won't look back, (though others might to admire you).

CHILD TEST: Observe often the shining *Inner Beauty* that irradiates the faces of young children. And know for a fact that the same joy, love and light that makes them glow is still within you, and always will be. They just need uncovering and releasing, and this *Beauty Plan* does that.

2. DON'T FLAUNT YOUR BEAUTY

Humility highlights beauty, flaunting beauty debases it. So to light up the room when you enter rather than when you leave, modesty's the key.

3. HANDLING THE ATTENTION BEAUTY BRINGS

Many believe that being radiantly beautiful would be the most wonderful thing in the world. And it is when you're glowing with true *Inner Beauty*; it's then also the most *natural* thing. However some find it difficult handling the extra attention that beauty can bring, especially if they're shy. Just as you can only be as truly beautiful as your inner happiness, you can only be as truly happy as living an *Inner Beauty*-centred life. And in releasing *Inner Beauty*, you also release more peace, serenity and self-confidence. And the additional composure and self-assurance they bring are your best shield for living comfortably with unwanted attention.

CHAPTER 3

11 INNER BEAUTY

WHOLE-LIFE

BONUSES

WHEN YOU UNCOVER
YOUR TRUE INNER BEAUTY,
YOU UNVEIL ALL YOUR
WHOLE-LIFE QUALITIES:

The beauty of increased ENERGY & EFFICIENCY — 63

The beauty of increased CONFIDENCE — 65

The beauty of increased HEALTH & LONGEVITY — 67

The beauty of increased WILLPOWER — 69

The beauty of increased PEACE & SERENITY — 71

The beauty of increased MEMORY — 73

The beauty of increased FRIENDSHIPS & LOVE — 75

The beauty of increased WISDOM & INTUITION — 77

The beauty of increased CREATIVITY — 79

The beauty of increased PROSPERITY — 81

The beauty of increased HAPPINESS — 83

'Exuberance is beauty' – William Blake

THE BEAUTY
OF INCREASED ENERGY
& EFFICIENCY

Increased energy and efficiency dramatically affect our everyday living; the more we have, the more empowered we feel and the more we achieve. The *Inner Beauty* practices have the two-fold ability to reduce your energy burn and hence conserve precious energy, while supercharging you with *new* energy.

Energy is life force. And by binding your mind to each moment *NOW*, the *PA* practice connects you to ever-new bites of life force. Whereas uncontrolled thoughts and worries drain your energy, by replacing mindlessness with mind*ful*ness the *PA* lifts your energy and efficiency.

Meditation is a powerful energy booster and saver too, because it dissolves energy-leaching stress, rush and worry.

The Beauty Mind Bathing (BMB) practices are great energy savers and revitalisers as well. For example, what's the ideal remedy for that lazy, lethargic, Sunday afternoon feeling? An uplifting **BMB** trip to delightful gardens, countryside, seaside or other local beauty spot. Or a dip into your beauty and happiness scrapbooks.

BMB visualisations and affirmations are immensely

energising. Athletes and business (wo)men use them to dig for their deepest depths of energy to achieve more. So can you. And we all know how revivifying a good read can be. Or listening to your favourite music.

In her wonderful little book *365 Ways to Energize Mind, Body & Soul*, Stephanie Tourles says, '… you can see the sun's energy as light, feel it as warmth… You can hear the invisible energy of thunder… and see purple bolts of lightning… Energy is vital. Energy is power.'

Sufficient sleep and exercise and a balanced diet are vital for maintaining energy. But you need more to counter the demands of today's rush and stress. The *Inner Beauty* practices meet those demands.

As you start saving and generating more and more energy, you'll notice it increasing your efficiency. You'll see something else too, how it beautifies your face and delights loved ones, family and friends.

'A new life begins for us with every second' – Jerome K Jerome

THE BEAUTY OF
INCREASED CONFIDENCE

Confidence is essential to your well being and success. When it's high and your mind at ease, you are happier, achieve more and shine. When it slips, doubts arise, you achieve less and your beauty covers over.

Confidence is a true soul quality. So the more *Inner Beauty* you uncover and release, the more natural confidence you unfold to light up your whole life.

Lack of confidence is mostly due to negative and limited ideas you hold about yourself. Because the mind and heart are so powerful, the longer you hang on to those ideas and feelings, the more you set them in concrete. Eventually they become your 'reality', no longer mere ideas but what you believe you *are*, believe you can or cannot do. You can and must shift those ideas.

I have a personal example of this: Through my childhood and teens I couldn't swim. 'If I jump into the water I'll sink,' I believed. And I did. At around the age of 20, I decided I'd learn to swim come hell or high water. (Gulp!) After months of perseverance I finally learnt. What changed? Just my *thinking*! When I believed I'd sink I sank, but now I believe I'll float and I do. That's the mighty power of the mind at work.

The *PA* arrests *uncontrolled* negative thinking by constantly returning you to the *NOW*. This dissolves negative-thinking habits to let your real *Inner Beauty* nature of confidence emerge. There will be things that undermined your confidence years ago that don't now. Why? Because more pressing concerns have replaced them and they've disappeared. Similarly, the *PA* can be put to use to dissolve your current worries *NOW*!

Meditation also lifts your confidence by stilling your mind and restoring your natural inner peace and joy.

The **Beauty Mind Bathing** visualisation exercise raises confidence too. Vividly picture yourself successfully achieving goals and overcoming personal stumbling blocks. What you can visualise you can actualise.

When your confidence increases you start restoring the natural shine of your *Inner Beauty*. You'll love it, and so will your loved ones and friends.

'The best and most beautiful things in the World cannot be seen or even touched. They must be felt with the heart' – Helen Keller

THE BEAUTY OF INCREASED HEALTH & LONGEVITY

Naturally, a balanced diet and sufficient sleep and exercise are essential for good health and longevity. But stress and negative thinking and emotions – the powerful psychophysical influences of mind over matter – can take a serious toll on our health. And when the usual remedial treatment is yet more pills and drugs, I worry about their long term effects on our finely-tuned, chemically-balanced bodies. Prevention has to be better than cure. And all three *Inner Beauty* practices are natural neutralisers of stress and negative thinking and emotions.

The PA plays many beneficial roles. By keeping you focused in the NOW, it squeezes uncontrolled worry from your mind; less worry, better health and longer life.

And by increasing your efficiency, the PA lightens your workload to help reduce stress.

SOUNDER EATING WITH THE PA: When you taste with attention your taste buds tell you what you need and when you've had enough. Obey and you keep healthier and live longer; trimmer too, more alert and bright-eyed. And you don't use precious energy in digesting and detoxifying superfluous waste.

MORE EFFICIENT EXERCISE WITH THE *PA*: Choose exercises you enjoy and you'll look forward to them. Group exercise and sports also extend your social life and increase friendships. Whatever exercises you choose, the *PA* increases your focus and efficiency.

MORE RESTFUL SLEEP: By neutralising stress and stilling your mind, all the *Inner Beauty* practices improve the quality of your sleep. And hence your health.

Meditation is renowned for its health-giving attributes which the research in the index on pages 85-86 verifies. And the **Beauty Mind Bathing** exercises promote good health in the same way, feeding the mind and heart with regular doses of re-energising positivity.

Good health both extends your life and gives it a *higher quality* through all your years. And when you glow with good health your facial beauty is at its best.

*Eliza in 'My Fair Lady' moved from the street to the elite through
perseverance. Willpower conquers all.*

THE BEAUTY OF
INCREASED WILLPOWER

The increased willpower released when uncovering your
Inner Beauty is one of your mightiest assets. For there's little you
can't overcome when you harness tenacious willpower. A proven
method of building willpower is by habitually achieving small
tasks. Tasks as rudimentary as unscrewing tight jar lids, threading
needles, and getting a stubborn chain back on a bicycle. Minor
things that arise in everyday life which we often give up on. Well,
persevere to help build the willpower habit.

Resisting temptations builds this habit too. Say no to extra
food helpings, chocolates, cigarettes, drinks, 'must have' new
shoes, watching poor TV, etc. Break the habits and you increase
your willpower.

Summoning courage also strengthens willpower. e.g.,
speaking up for what you believe in or to support others, or
agreeing to give an off-the-cuff thank you speech.

Setting and achieving goals builds willpower as well. Goals
for getting fitter, losing or putting on weight, writing letters or
making phone calls you've been putting off, cleaning the car, etc.
Having set goals, don't let yourself down; achieve them. And as

you accomplish more, set larger goals and meet those too. This builds a chain of success that consolidates in your subconscious and superconscious mind to build formidable willpower.

What is willpower but the power of thoughts and feelings we bring under our will. So the more we control our minds and hearts, the more willpower we release.

All the above examples are greatly enhanced by practising the PA because of the increased focus it brings.

Meditation builds willpower too. The very act of repeatedly returning the mind to the focus of your meditation whenever it drifts off increases willpower.

And the **BMB** visualisation and affirmation exercises build willpower by helping cement goals in your mind's eye and thereby hastening their achievement.

Increased willpower promotes success in all areas of your life. And that brings a glow that lights up and beautifies your whole persona.

'I will speak no ill of any man, and all the good I can of everyone'
– Benjamin Franklin

THE BEAUTY OF
INCREASED PEACE
& SERENITY

When you embrace the three *Inner Beauty* practices, tranquillity starts to naturally arise from a deep well of calm that you can carry around for on-going sustenance.

CALMNESS & DRIVE: Calmness does not impede the drive needed for getting things done in today's fast-paced environment; the very opposite is true. Efficiency flows to the fore when you are *peacefully* active. And after mindfully and effectively completing an action with the requisite energy-efficient input, you can immediately return to the position of *active* peace. These alternate states promote balanced, harmonious and joyful living. Experience has shown you that you think most clearly when your mind is calm and clear, not when it's filled with myriad, uninvited, woolly thoughts and emotions.

The power accessible from our deep, still centre when we raise consciousness/awareness is enormous. In his book *Zen in the Art of Archery*, German professor, Eugen Herrigel, describes a striking example of this when he was tutored by a Japanese archery master in Tokyo. One night, when the target could not be seen some ten metres away in the darkened indoor range, the master archer hit the centre of the bulls eye not once but twice in a row, the second arrow slicing through the first.

That's exceptional mind power arising from stillness. Think what we might achieve by uncovering and releasing more of our *Inner Beauty* potency and lifting our current dismal 5-20% use of our mighty mind power.

Because peace and serenity are part of your true soul nature, whenever you come away from what you are *not* – their opposites, disquiet and turmoil – you automatically return to those states. And your best tools for doing this are **meditation** and the PA. They dissolve the habitual layers of ongoing chatter that befuddle the mind and create worries.

Nothing beautifies the face more than peace and serenity. And you release them in abundance when you uncover your *Inner Beauty*.

'The beauty that is within you cannot be contained' – Eileen Caddy

THE BEAUTY OF
INCREASED MEMORY

Memory plays a vital part in our lives because if we forget what we learn and experience, we lose their derived benefits. Here's how the *Inner Beauty* practices awaken and sharpen memory:

Reduced memory is primarily due to uncontrolled absence of mind when the event takes place, (excepting, of course, the natural affects of ageing and the likes of alzheimer's).

Practising the PA stops your mind from habitually drifting, and the increase in focus you bring to bear in each moment improves observation and hence memory. When the attention is childlike and outward, all your senses come alive. You perceive all the bursting of colour, form and action, the birdsong and smells, the vibrancy of creation. So your memory better recalls the moment. This graphic remembering can be likened to the way we least forget those joyous and sorrowful emotional moments that touch us most deeply.

Regular **meditation** also aids memory by helping still the mind and heart; agitation reduces our attentiveness and ability to take in data whereas a still, concentrating mind efficiently absorbs things.

The *BMB* visualisation exercises assist memory too, particularly to counter the thought 'I don't have a good memory.' Try the following exercises to counter forgetting people's names when being introduced, and misplacing things.

Visualise yourself:

– being introduced to people. You are fully attentive and repeat their names: 'Pleased to meet you, James,' etc. Calmly picture each person's face while inwardly repeating his or her name.

– placing down items like keys and mobile phone with full attention so you picture exactly where you put them.

In bed at night, replay the events of the day in your mind's eye. This is not only good for the memory, it's better than counting sheep for getting off to sleep.

When your memory increases so does your confidence which lifts your heart and lights up your face. That's what true beauty is about.

'My best friend is he who brings out the best in me.'
– Henry Ford, car manufacturer

THE BEAUTY OF
INCREASED FRIENDSHIPS & LOVE

True friendships are a key ingredient to a happy life, and certainly lack of friends can lead to loneliness.

Close friendships and love go hand-in-hand. The most soul-mated of loving couples say of each other: '(s)he's also my best friend.' So do many loving parents of their sons and daughters and vice-versa. So what makes a good friend? And how does practising the *Inner Beauty* exercises help attract friendships and loved ones?

Essentially, good friends enjoy one another's company. They usually have similar natures, values and interests, but not always, confirming that opposites can also attract. Close friends are comfortable and relaxed with one another, opening up hearts and minds without holding back. They help one another through thick and thin, lightening the daily load and general grind of life.

You can have a good laugh with them too because they usually share your sense of humour, and genuinely want to hear your experiences and your views on theirs. Part mentors and personal coaches, part confidants, they share your joys and troubles, uplifting you when your spirits are low. Most important, good friends don't let you let yourself down, they tell you straight.

People are naturally drawn to those who manifest a confident inner peace and joy. This is because these true imperishable soul characteristics are within us all, (albeit they're more covered over in some than others), and they magnetically attract, one to another. Because the qualities (or lack of) you carry in your mind and heart reflect in your face, when you uncover and express your *Inner Beauty* qualities, people with like qualities are naturally drawn to you. Can you imagine a stronger set of attractions for increasing friendships and finding that 'special one' who will become your loving mate?

Good friends are like precious jewels – priceless assets and a joy forever. And uncovering your *Inner Beauty* attracts them. Ralph Waldo Emerson said, 'The only way to have a friend is to be one.' And you'll be that when you release and share your *Inner Beauty* qualities. Isn't that the way to best attract your soul mate?

'Wisdom is of the soul' – Walt Whitman

THE BEAUTY
OF INCREASED KNOWLEDGE,
WISDOM & INTUITION

The extent to which we can access knowledge, wisdom and intuition profoundly influences our lives. And access is greatly enhanced by practising the *Inner Beauty* exercises. Knowledge is knowing the how, why, what, where, when, and who of people, places, events and things. Wisdom is the wise, discriminating application of knowledge that's needed to solve our problems. Intuition is insightful, infallible, soul-fed wisdom that penetrates beyond the fallible intellect.

INCREASED KNOWLEDGE: The reason you know more about the things you like most in life is because you give them more attention. And when you use the PA to free your mind of uncontrolled chatter, your greater focus increases your knowledge of everything. You retain more knowledge too because your memory works more efficiently. By dissolving restlessness. **Meditation** also makes the mind receptive for absorbing knowledge.

INCREASED WISDOM & INTUITION: We all want to be wiser because we need answers to our everyday challenges. For this we need to tune into the intuitive wisdom of our true soul nature which operates best when our emotions and thoughts are brought to rest with the *PA* and **meditation**. Ultimate wisdom draws on intuition. Paramahansa Yogananda, the superman saint of the Twentieth Century, wrote: '... Intelligence interprets... the outward appearance of things... but in deep inner perception, where the senses and intellect cannot reach, intuition prevails. ... Intuition is the rein of power behind all of man's mental phenomena – thought, attention, will, sensation, perception, memory... feelings, impulses. ... Intuition is soul guidance, appearing naturally in man during those instants when his mind is calm. ...Meditation is what develops the Calm Inner Light of intuitive divine perception.'*

There's something uniquely beautiful about a wisdom-filled mind that enlivens the face. And uncovering your *Inner Beauty* releases it.

Excerpts from his 'Autobiography of a Yogi' and commentaries on 'The Bhagavad Gita'.

'Art washes from the soul the dust of everyday life.' – Picasso

THE BEAUTY OF
INCREASED CREATIVITY

It's not just the 'artists' of this world who need creativity, we all do, because we all have problems that need ideas for their resolution. Creativity in its usual context, though, has two main aspects: creative excellence and new concepts/ideas. The *Inner Beauty* practices help maximise both.

CREATIVE EXCELLENCE: Creative excellence is attained by learning and perfecting the techniques and dexterity required of the art. For this – innate talent aside – full application is essential. And that needs sustained concentration and effort that the mind/heart-controlling *PA* and **meditation** provide. Artists then go on to create their best works with *PA*-applied 100% attention.

The visualisation exercises of **Beauty Mind Bathing** work directly to increase artistic excellence too. For what you can visualise, you can actualise.

The more vividly a painter pictures the desired result in the mind's eye, the greater the drive and ability to turn it into reality.

Likewise with musicians who visualise successfully performing demanding pieces of music to audiences. It aids the drive of practising to perfection to achieve that very result.

NEW CONCEPTS & IDEAS: This is where the PA comes into its own. It's the best practice I know for keeping your mind *empty*, chatter-free and ready and receptive for logging on to new sparks of inspiration when they arise: in this state it is ready-tuned to capture things new in the air* or fed from within by the subconscious or superconscious mind that work quietly 'behind the scenes' to deliver when ready. But they can't deliver if no one is at home, i.e. if your mind is absent; no presence, no presents!

This is the key to maximising ideas. If your mind is full of uninvited, uncontrolled, circling thoughts, there's no room for new ideas to fly in and take nest.

When you produce your best creative work and light up with ideas, you really start to sparkle; then you're a picture of beauty.

---

*Much evidence supports the concept of universal mind – an interconnectivity among all separate minds. Many inventions, for example, down through history, were created during the same periods in different countries before those countries even knew the others existed. And the occurrence of two or more people getting the same idea at the same time, is commonplace.

'Let the beauty we love be what we do.' – Rumi

THE BEAUTY OF
INCREASED PROSPERITY

By accessing greater mind and heart power to uncover and release your *Inner Beauty*, you also increase prosperity in every aspect of your life.

The reason lies in what you unearth from within – joy, love, peace, integrity, generosity and the other attributes outlined earlier. Picture a young child glowing with these shining qualities and you immediately appreciate their magnetic power of attraction. And attraction is what attaining prosperity is all about.

PROSPERITY IN FRIENDSHIPS: When you exhibit *Inner Beauty* qualities, people with like qualities are naturally drawn to you and you to them. And it's invariably with these people that trusting, life-long friendships are made. Without true friends, no life could be considered prosperous, and with them, even in times of deepest troubles and greatest needs, you can still count yourself prosperous.

PARTNER PROSPERITY: For the same reasons, releasing your *Inner Beauty* qualities increases your chances of attracting that extra special friend who becomes your loving and loyal partner. The support that (s)he can inspire makes the world of difference to really enjoying life, managing its tribulations and coming out on top. The adage of a key to success being the right partner behind one, is a cliché because it's true.

ALROUND PROSPERITY: When *Inner Beauty*-induced prosperity gathers momentum in one area of your life, it spreads to others because success breeds success. When greater mind/heart control conquers stress and strain, your health improves; you sleep better, eat better, feel better, look better. Your energy and efficiency increase, and you become sharper, more creative, more articulate.

Then your confidence grows in leaps and bounds, along with your career. And for most of us, this is the essence of prosperity, career success and financial security. And where does this lead? To happiness, the true measure of prosperity. For whereas all the money in the world cannot buy happiness, happiness is in itself prosperity. And it beautifies you through and through.

*'Whilst the peoples of the world speak in a multitude of different
languages, they all laugh in only one'*
— Tony Russell

THE BEAUTY OF
INCREASED HAPPINESS
& SENSE OF HUMOUR

Happiness is the underlying purpose of everything we do, our ultimate goal. And because it's part of our true soul nature as we looked at in Chapter One, the sooner we stop vainly seeking it 'out there' and practise the *Inner Beauty* exercises, the sooner we uncover it and thrive in its child-like fun and joy.

A good sense of humour is essential to happiness. We love to laugh, and humour instantly cuts through negativity, lifts the spirits, relaxes and refreshes, and restores a healthy balance to heart and mind.

By reinstating peace and stillness, regular **meditation** arouses a gentle objectivity that keeps the 'tragedies' of life in perspective. This lightens your viewpoint, allowing humour to arise about things that might once have upset you. This is the beauty of the PA too; the greater presence of mind it brings enables you to detach from life's unpleasantness and enjoy its myriad fun moments.

It's wonderful, isn't it, running into an acquaintance who

delights you with happy incidents and anecdotes and makes you laugh. You walk on feeling really cheerful. Collectively, such instances not only build up habits of released happiness but send out positive vibrations that enhance the world at large. (And what a contrast to the woebegones you meet whose criticisms and lowly thoughts leave you feeling unworthy or despondent.)

An excellent and rewarding **Beauty Mind Bathing** practice is to treat humour as an art form by collecting jokes, and looking for the humour in situations you previously might have judged. Notice how those who don't get upset whatever the situation tend to have a good sense of humour. Deep inner calm savours humour and thrives on it. Encourage and develop yours with the *Inner Beauty* practices and you'll thrive on it too.

Happiness is the very essence of your *Inner Beauty*. And just as you can only be as beautiful as your inner happiness, you can only be as happy as the *Inner Beauty* you uncover. Now you have the tools to do it.

APPENDIX

1. COMPELLING SCIENTIFIC EVIDENCE OF MEDITATION'S BENEFITS

Most of the meditation research that's been carried out around the world is on Transcendental Meditation (TM). It is awesome in its breadth and depth: more than 600* studies over 30 years at 230 research institutes in 24 countries. Here's a mere fraction of its findings:

Some effects of Transcendental Meditation:

GENERAL:
- A unique state of deep rest.
- Increased relaxation, efficiency and self-confidence.
- Elevated mood and greater mental clarity.
- Greater emotional stability.
- Increased alertness and wakefulness, and faster reaction times.
- Experiences of higher states of consciousness.

HEALTH:
- Reduced blood pressure and cholesterol levels.
- Reduced breath rate and oxygen consumption.
- Reduced metabolism in muscle tissue.
- Large increase in cardiac output.
- Stress reduction.
- Unique pattern of DNA repair.
- Improvement of bronchial asthma.
- Diabetes treatment and prevention through more efficient glucose homeostasis.
- Better periodontal (dental) health.
- Overweight people lost weight and underweight gained, pointing to normalisation of body functioning; and increased effectiveness of dietary treatment for obesity.
- Improved psycho-social health.
- Decreased neuroticism and personality disorder.
- Reduced consumption of tobacco, alcohol and prescribed (including tranquillisers) and non-prescribed drugs.

SLEEP:
- Reduced sleep required.
- Decreased insomnia.
- Improved quality of sleep.
- Faster recovery from sleep deprivation.

* *Maharishi International University, Fairfield, Iowa, USA.*

PREGNANCY & CHILDBIRTH:
- Pregnancy: reduced pain and fewer complaints.
- Childbirth: shorter labour, less anxiety, less pain.

BUSINESS:
- Increased efficiency and productivity.
- Reduced job worry and tension.
- Improved work relationships.

EDUCATION:
- Enhanced concentration and reading comprehension.
- Enhanced memory and creativity.
- Increased self-confidence.

CHILDREN:
- Less depression, anxiety, nervousness and fatigue.
- Less aggressiveness, anger and dreaminess.
- Greater self-control and ability to focus.
- Greater emotional maturity.

SPORT:
- Athletes show reduction in heart rate, respiration rate, oxygen consumption, carbon dioxide elimination.

ELDERLY:
- Reversal of ageing: short term (3 years) meditators' biological age was 5 years younger; long term (7+ years) meditators' biological age was 12 years younger.
- Greater sense of well being and higher degree of mental alertness.
- Improved neurological efficiency.
- Improved visual perception and auditory discrimination.
- Faster reactions and fewer mistakes.
- Increased word fluency.
- Fewer in-patient admissions for all major diseases.

In conclusion, I am aware of no research study that says meditation is not good for you.

SOME MEDIA COMMENTS ON
MEDITATION GOING RIGHT BACK TO 1988

(EXCERPTS FROM *THE DAILY TELEGRAPH* NEWSPAPER ARTICLE
OF 10.11.'99 BY DR SARAH BREWER, GP)

A CALMING INFLUENCE

DEAR DOCTOR – I suffer from high blood pressure linked with stress and am considering trying transcendental meditation. Can you tell me whether it is likely to help?

(Dr Brewer's response): Meditation uses a variety of mental techniques to attain a state of complete relaxation. The form known as transcendental meditation (TM) ... helps the user still their thoughts and find a deeper level of consciousness, while remaining fully alert. It leaves you feeling refreshed mentally and physically, calmer and able to think more clearly. An analysis of 28 studies published in Hypertension – the journal of the American Heart Association – showed that TM reduced highest pumping blood pressure by an average of 11 mmHg and relaxed BP (blood pressure) by 6 mmHg within three months. It also reduces stress, anxiety and cholesterol levels and improves quality of sleep, as well as helping people cut back on, or stop, smoking, drinking or drug abuse. ...

(EXCERPTS FROM OCTOBER 2000 *"RED MAGAZINE"*
BY EDITOR, SALLY BRAMPTON)

FREE YOUR MIND

It began with insomnia. ... I had just taken over as the editor of this (Red) magazine, with all its attendant delights and pressures. ... Karena Callen, the former Beauty Director of this magazine, took one look at my bleary eyes and drawn face and said, 'You need to meditate.' ... I sign up for the course. ... it is the personal benefits of TM that are so compelling. There was a time, after a hard day's work, I used to hurry home for a large glass of white wine. Now, I hurry home to meditate. It doesn't eradicate all the scratchy irritations of the day ... but it does make them much easier to deal with. And each time you meditate it's different. Sometimes you feel wonderfully calm, other times peaceful, and at others full of optimism and joy (neither of which come easily to me). ...Madonna, Demi Moore and Trudie Styler are all devotees. ...Business entrepreneur and trouble-shooter Sir John Harvey-Jones is one of its most vociferous advocates. ... What I do know is that meditation is, for me anyway, an intense and private joy.

'IT CHANGED MY LIFE'

... some 600 British GPs who practise TM had written to the government urging that it be made available on the NHS. ... But what most impressed me were the interviews I conducted with a number of meditators ... They cited benefits including the ability to handle stress, feelings of calm, relaxation and general well-being, resistance to colds and flu, and the ability to think more clearly, to get down to things and accomplish more. ... While meditation is itself enjoyable, the real benefits come afterwards. ... My partner noticed immediately that I had become happier ... calmer. My concentration has improved, I have amazing energy ... I feel more patient and tolerant ... able to control my anger and frustration ...Meditation is said to slow the ageing process. That I cannot assess, but after a couple of weeks I met an acquaintance of 15 years. "You look well," she said. A pause while she studied me intently. "I haven't seen you looking so well in ages." Another pause. "In fact, I've never seen you look this well before."

EXCERPTS FROM PETER J CONRADI'S ARTICLE,
LONDON *EVENING STANDARD*, 27.1. 2004

THE DAY I LEARNED TO THINK MYSELF BETTER

How one writer, plagued by a series of panic attacks, discovered the extraordinary power of meditation.

... I recall that first sensation well. Getting onto the Underground made me sweat with fear. ... A panic attack over those following (15) years could hit me at any time. ... I found a (Buddhism) meditation centre near where I live. ... The basic meditation technique is called "calm abiding". It is simply described, but nonetheless powerful... It can be shocking to see how busy the mind is, endlessly playing truant like a naughty schoolchild. ... Meditation emphasises the essential workability of all situations, so obstacles can turn into challenges. It makes you softer, kinder, more patient. ... The effects of all this – over months and years – can be profound. ... you gradually learn to outface your fears.

MIND THE GAPS

TM is a technique you learn, like driving a car. You don't have to believe in it; indeed you can think it's a load of old rope but if you do it, it will work. ... I like to think that after 15 years ... my work has improved and that I am indeed the sunshine of our home. Little knots of worry loosen: a fear of sleeping in the house alone, a fear of death, grudges borne over years, stabs of guilt about the past. You think of these things and come to realise that they've gone. One is surprised by new insights. ... Then there is bliss. This is an irrational happiness that floods the system – my system all too rarely, but enough to know what it's like. And when you feel it, you realise you had it as a child. When you have this feeling on the London Underground in the middle of the rush-hour, you know you're really getting somewhere.

EXCERPTS FROM CHRISTINE DOYLE'S ARTICLE IN THE 'HEALTH & WELLBEING' COLUMN OF THE DAILY TELEGRAPH, OCTOBER 7, 2003

'IT WAS A TOTALLY NUMBING TIME'

Zoe Lindgren was diagnosed with breast cancer 15 years ago. She was 31 and six months' pregnant with her second child. She refused an abortion and had a partial mastectomy. In 1991, tests revealed a second tumour in her lungs which had also spread to her lymphatic system. "...Chemotherapy, I was told, might give me another two years, but there were no guarantees," she says. "I decided not to have this treatment ... it was a totally numbing time." She decided, despite her fear and confusion, that she had to take control herself . ... Her first step was to visit Dr. Daniel, who was Medical Director of the Bristol Cancer Help Centre at the time. "On her advice, I became a vegetarian and took vitamins, supplements and herbs. A course of acupuncture helped to restore my red blood cells to normal levels. I went through a radical shift in my perception to embrace the holistic approach and the power of self-healing." She learnt to meditate, at a Buddhist centre. ... "Meditation taught me that fear wasn't necessary and it stopped me thinking negatively. Once I started meditating, I ceased to be depressed which can affect the body physically, and coped more easily with stress."

A VISUALISATION EXERCISE:
WALKING THROUGH A MAGICAL GARDEN

I am completely at peace with the world. The sun is shining, warming me from top to toe. I start wandering through the gardens in which, by some stroke of genius, the most exquisite flowers and shrubs of all four seasons are in full bloom at once. The colours, textures, and heavenly perfumes are breathtaking.

I meander through a wild, mini meadowland where carpets of bluebells, snowdrops, crocuses, primroses, daffodils and tulips, bloom in full resplendent colour.

I ascend steps and wander beneath a pergola festooned with climbing roses of every colour. They reach from ankle to shoulder and canopy above my head to form a long natural bower. Bending to smell each variety, I'm repeatedly enveloped in divine perfume.

I emerge from the pergola on to a patio, dappled-shaded by a giant, heavenly-scented Mock Orange. Beneath it a smiling waiter beckons me over to sit and enjoy a long cool drink and delicious cakes. How can I resist? I don't. I would linger longer but my desire to see the rest of the garden presses me on.

Within ten paces I'm overlooking an exquisite walled garden, teeming with colour. I walk down the steps, admiring the overhead full flowering wisteria, honeysuckle and dozen different clematis intertwining with yellow winter and white summer jasmine. At the bottom I gasp again. To my left, butterflies flutter over deep red and mauve Budleah cones, masses of stately Delphiniums, giant Lupins, Foxgloves, Holly Hocks and Canterbury Bells.

To my right, Sunflowers tower over pink and white Japanese Anemones, Peonies, Cosmea, Evening Primroses, Irises, Dahlias, Phlox and orange and red Crocosmia, all in flourishing full bloom. I saunter, gape and softly shake my head in amazement. Surely this is a miracle.

Every step reveals more full-bloom grandeur. Giant Camellias and Rhododendrons, Azaleas, blue Ceanothus, pink, blue and white Cistus, myriad varieties of Hebe with blue, pink and white florets, dazzling yellow Forsythia, Hypericum, Mahonia and Spanish Broom; Lilacs, and blue, pink and creamy-white lace-cap and mop head Hydrangeas.

And around and beneath these wondrous sun-drenched plants, cluster upon cluster of my favourite annual and perennial flowers stake their claims in this magical realm. Delicate, luminous Petunias, Wallflowers, Forget-me-nots, Cornflowers, Carnations, Marigolds, Nasturtiums, Violets and Pansies, Verbena, Geraniums, Stocks, Nicotiana, Poppies, Daisies and Irises. And the Lilies, so many varieties! I pinch myself. Am I in heaven? I surely am.

A VISUALISATION EXERCISE:
HOLIDAYING IN A PACIFIC ISLAND
SHANGRI-LA

How I love this part of the island. Quiet, peaceful, serene and so beautiful. I park the car and amble through the short stretch of green undergrowth, refreshingly cool beneath the lofty palms. I soon emerge on to the beach and into the sun.

The soft white sand, warm beneath my feet, pushes up between my toes. As always, first sight of the full panoramic vista of the crescent-shaped bay and the sea and sky beyond takes my breath away. It's my favourite time of the day when the late afternoon sun shows its gentler side yet is still deliciously warm.

The beach is deserted apart from the two young boys, fishing again with their father off the end of the short wooden jetty. I'd heard their squeals of laughter when I opened the car door. Their catches of fish are usually small, but every success draws joyous rapture.

The sunlight is dancing off the small waves rippling gently into shore. The crystal clear turquoise sea stretches uninterrupted to the horizon where a small, dark, steely-grey cloud intensifies the azure blue sky.

I sigh and breathe in deeply. Only three days into my break from the daily city grind, and all my pent up tensions and cares are dissolving like sherbet on the tongue. I reflect on my mind's foolish city entrapment. My long sigh breaks into an irrepressible laugh, loud enough for the boys to look up and wave. I wave back and amble towards them.

Three weeks, three! I've never had such a long holiday. And never one as already so promising. Everything on the island is perfect: the scenery, the weather, the hotel, the food, the people. Yes, especially the people. So warm and friendly, so genuine, uninhibited and outgoing, sharing their cheeriness and enfolding me like family with love and affection. And there are still two and a half weeks to go. I sigh once more and quicken my pace. The boys are squealing with delight again and I want to join in the fun.

THREE VISUALISATIONS FOR DISSOLVING UNPLEASANT MEMORIES:

1 ....(name the experience) **is like a leaden lump in my stomach. This is no longer acceptable.**

Visualise placing a large effervescent lozenge that has a strong, happy face on it, into a glass of water where it dissolves, fizzing away with a gurgling chuckle. You drink the fizzy concoction, feeling it warm your throat and gullet as it descends to your tummy. Repeating the affirmation:

> *Leaden lump chew up and flee,*
> *You no longer bother me,*

feel the fizzy concoction getting to grips with your leaden lump, chewing it up, until it completely disappears. Now burp, expelling away the last of the leaden lump forever.

2 ....(name the experience) **is an ongoing ache in my heart. This is no longer acceptable.**

Vigorously rub together the palms and fingers of your open hands, one hand against the other, for thirty seconds. Place your warmed-up hands over your heart while repeating this affirmation:

> *Heartache flee – away with you!*
> *I am starting life anew.*

Feel the heat of your hands burning adrift the heartache. Now breathe out long breaths to expel away the heartache forever.

3 ....(name the experience) **is a huge pressure on my mind. This is no longer acceptable.**

Vigorously rub together the palms and fingers of your open hands, one hand against the other, for thirty seconds. Place your warmed-up hands on top of your head while repeating this affirmation:

> *Fly out pressures, fly in peace,*
> *All my cares I now release.*

Feel the heat and pressure of your hands pushing out the pressure from your mind until it has all gone. All the while, breathe out as you visualise your pressures flying out of you, and breathe in as you visualise strength and peace flying in.

GENERAL DIRECTIONS FOR
BMB AFFIRMATIONS:

1. Affirmations should be clear, precise and as punchy as possible to help memorability and assimilation. Belief in their power is essential. There's no point in repeating, for example, *'Every day in every way I'm releasing my Inner Beauty,'* if you don't believe you possess *Inner Beauty*. (In this particular case reassure yourself that you do by looking again at your soul qualities on page 3.)

2. Phrase affirmations in the present tense: *'I am releasing my Inner Beauty'*; not *'I will release my Inner Beauty.'*

3. The affirmations will penetrate deep into your subconscious and super-conscious mind if you repeat them often daily, especially before going to bed and when you arise.

AFFIRMATIONS:

1. **For helping release your true soul qualities:**
   (choose singularly or combine, or use your own words):
   *Every day in every way I am releasing my **Inner Beauty** ...my **Happiness** ... my **Self Confidence** ...my **Willpower** ...my **Peace and Serenity** ...my **Creativity** ...my **Wisdom & Intuition** ...my **Prosperity**.*

2. **As above, but expressed another way:**
   *Within me is the storehouse of **infinite Beauty** ...**infinite Happiness** ...**infinite Confidence** ...**infinite Willpower** ...**infinite Peace and Serenity** ...**infinite Creativity** ...**infinite Wisdom & Intuition** ...**infinite Prosperity**.*

3. **Affirmation for burying the past and starting afresh:**
   Today is the first day of the rest of my life.

4. **Affirmation to help accelerate health & healing:**
   Every day in every way I am getting better and better.
   Every day in every way I am growing stronger and stronger.

5. **Affirmation for confirming specific qualities/skills/etc.:**
   Every day in every way my ....(name the quality/skill)
   is getting better and better.
   I am joy, I am light, I am love, I am .... (add to, if you wish.)
   I am bubbling over with joy, light and love.
   I am bubbling over with .... (choose inspiring words
   from page 96 or use your own words.)
   I am tuning into creativity.
   I am tuning into .... (choose inspiring words
   from page 96 or use your own words.)

6. **Affirmation of Gratitude:**

   I have so much to be grateful for: ....(name the things, people, events, etc. as appropriate).

   I count my blessings: .... (name them).

7. **Affirmation for overcoming JOB LOSS:**

   I know that when one door closes another opens, so I am seeing this as a new opportunity to start afresh. What I have achieved before I can achieve again. I am eliminating worry because that inhibits the mind and heart clarity I need to maximise my creativity and efficiency for finding new openings. Every day I'm taking practical steps to increase opportunities by speaking to friends, networking, reviewing job ads, and contacting companies and job agencies. I have much to offer a new employer and will make them proud and thankful for taking me on.

   I have excellent work skills and experience: ....
   ....(speak and write them).

   I count all my blessings too: .... (speak and write them).

   It is vital to stay upbeat and retain my self-confidence so I'm practising the three Inner Beauty exercises daily. I'm going to turn this situation into a triumph!

8. **Affirmation for overcoming DIVORCE/partner separation:**

   As others have before me, I will work through this and overcome the heartache, and resolve all the things I need to in my new situation. For the peace of mind and health of myself and everyone involved, especially my dependants, it's important to keep a grip on the situation; so I'm doing everything I can to stay positive and keep up my and everyone's spirits.

   I call upon my family and friends for support and advice, for they know, and I appreciate, that troubles shared are troubles halved. I keep reminding myself that I am no less a person now than I was a year ago. Every day I count and recall all my blessings: .... (speak and write them.)

   I'm practising the Inner Beauty exercises to help bring equilibrium back into my life.

   Hope springs eternal, and in the not too distant future I will be looking back to see I've made a successful new life for myself and my dependants, just as thousands of others have.

9. **Affirmation for overcoming LOSS OF A LOVED ONE:**

   I know that .... *(loved one) would not want me to be unhappy and in despair so I'm making my best efforts to get over the situation, and do all I can to dignify* ....*'s (loved one) memory by recalling and glorifying his/her qualities. That said, I know it is natural and important to my health to grieve and not be in denial. So I'm being patient with myself and allowing this process to take its course. I'm also practising the Inner Beauty exercises to help bring back the equilibrium into my life.*

10. Affirmation to reduce the worry of MOVING HOUSE:

I am eliminating the worry by getting really organised and keeping my heart and mind positively focused on the benefits, new opportunities and sheer fun of the move. I'm asking friends to advise me from their experiences on the do's and don'ts for moving. And I'm making, and constantly adding to lists of all the things I need to do – and avoid – and following up with the action. Yes, I'm going to turn this move into a big success!

SOME INSPIRING WORDS
FOR USE IN AFFIRMATIONS

ADD YOUR OWN WORDS TOO;
JUST READING THROUGH THIS LIST CAN BE UPLIFTING:

Abundance, Acceptance, Adaptable, Adventure, Appreciation, Aspire, Assertive, Balance, Beauty, Breakthrough, Calm, Caring, Change, Cheerful, Choice, Clarity, Comfort, Commitment, Compassion, Completing, Cooperation, Confidence, Consistent, Contentment, Courage, Creative, Decisive, Delight, Dependable, Disciplined, Discovery, Ease, Efficiency, Encouragement, Enriched, Empowered, Enjoy, Enthusiasm, Excellence, Expectancy, Experience, Exuberance, Faith, Family, Flexible, Focus, Forgiveness, Forthright, Freedom, Friends, Fulfilling, Fun, Generosity, Gentle, Grace, Gratitude, Growth, Happiness, Harmony, Harvest, Healing, Honesty, Hope, Humility, Humour, Ideas, Inspiration, Integrity, Intelligence, Involvement, Joy, Kindness, Knowledge, Laughter, Light, Love, Magnificence, Maturity, Motivation, Nourish, Nurture, Openness, Optimistic, Opportunity, Order, Organised, Partnership, Patience, Peace, Perseverance, Power, Practical, Progress, Play, Prosperity, Purity, Purpose, Readiness, Reassurance, Recognition, Rejoicing, Relationships, Relaxation, Release, Resolution, Resourceful, Responsible, Rest, Results, Satisfaction, Security, Self-esteem, Serenity, Service, Sharing, Sincere, Solutions, Spontaneous, Stability, Steadfast, Strength, Success, Support, Tenderness, Thorough, Tolerant, Triumph, Trust, Truth, Understanding, Unity, Versatility, Vision, Vitality, Wealth, Willingness, Wisdom, Worth.

NOTES

NOTES

NOTES

NOTES

NOTES

NOTES

NOTES